A personal statement

Write a **sentence** in answer to each of these questions.

1 What is your full name?

_____.

2 How old are you?

_____.

3 What is the colour of your eyes?

_____.

4 Are you **tall** or **short** or **just average height** for your age?

_____.

5 Which class are you in at school?

_____.

6 As you write this, are you **at home**, **at school** or **at a friend's house**?

_____.

7 Are you **alone** or is there **someone with you**?

_____.

8 What are you writing with, — **a pen** or **a pencil**?

_____.

9 Are you **left-handed** or **right-handed**?

_____.

10 Are you wearing **boots**, **shoes**, **sandals** or **slippers**?

_____.

Ask your friend to read this statement and, if it is correct, to sign it here as a witness.

> I agree that this statement is correct.
>
> Signature_____   Date_____

Name each one

artist   castle   eagle   guitar   iron

bottle   donkey   fence   hinge   jeans

From this list write the correct name under each picture.

Youngsters

Here are pictures of ten creatures.

Here are the names — not in order — of the young of these creatures.

calf	cub	foal	kitten	puppy
chicken	cygnet	kid	lamb	tadpole

Using the number on the picture, write a sentence linking each creature and its young. The first one is done for you.

1 *A young cat is called a kitten* _____.

2 _____.

3 _____.

4 _____.

5 _____.

6 _____.

7 _____.

8 _____.

9 _____.

10 _____.

Words starting with wh

A Write the correct word under each picture, using one letter in each square.

| w | h | | | |

| | | | t |

| | | | | p | |

| | | | | |

| | | s | t | | |

| | | | t |

| | | | k | | |

| | | p |

| | | | | | y |

| What | When | Where | Which | Who | Whose | Why |

B Choose the correct word from this list to write as the first word in each of these questions.

1 _____ way is it to the station, please?

2 _____ have you left your hat and coat?

3 _____ are you doing?

4 _____ has taken my ruler?

5 _____ is the sun so hot?

6 _____ will my watch be ready?

7 _____ parents are coming to the concert?

Page 4

Words starting with wh

Helen and Lance are talking to Mr. Jackson, the railway porter.

In asking him questions, they use these words beginning with **wh**.

what	where	which	who	whose
when	whether	while	whole	why

From this list, write the correct word in their questions.

After each question, write down what you think Mr. Jackson said in reply.

1 *Helen:* "Hello, Mr. Jackson._____are you doing with that brush?"

   Mr. J.: "_____."

2 *Lance:* "Do you have to sweep the_____of the station?"

   Mr. J.: "_____."

3 *Helen:* "_____tells you_____you have to do?"

   Mr. J.: "_____."

4 *Lance:* "Can you please tell me_____train comes in next?"

   Mr. J.: "_____."

5 *Helen:* "_____does it go_____it leaves here?"

   Mr. J.: "_____."

6 *Lance:* "_____luggage is that over there?"

   Mr. J.: "_____."

7 *Helen:* "Do you know_____they are coming back for it or not?"

   Mr. J.: "_____."

8 *Lance:* "_____they are away, couldn't someone steal it?"

   Mr. J.: "_____."

9 *Helen:* "The train hasn't come yet. Do you know_____it is late?"

   Mr. J.: "_____."

10 *Helen and Lance:* "Thank you very much. We must go now. Goodbye."

   Mr. J.: "_____."

How are they the same?

banjo	fork	hoe	nail
case	guitar	knife	postcard
cup	handbag	letter	rake
fence	hedge	mug	screw

From this list write the correct name under each picture.

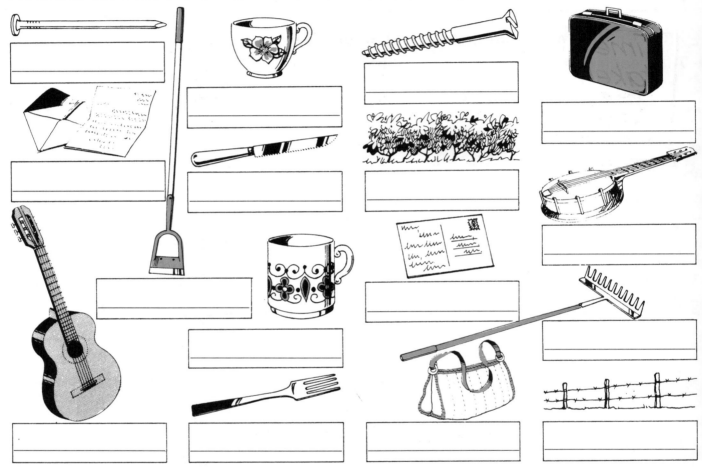

From the same list, write the names of two things in each of these sentences.

1 A_____ and a_____ are both used for fastening wood.

2 A_____ and a_____ are both used for sending messages.

3 A_____ and a_____ are both used for drinking.

4 A_____ and a_____ are both used for eating.

5 A_____ and a_____ are both used for gardening.

6 A_____ and a_____ are both used for carrying belongings

7 A_____ and a_____ are both used for making music.

8 A_____ and a_____ are both used for separating fields.

Telling the time

After each of these notices finish the sentence saying what the notice means.
Write the time in **words**.   You will need these words.

arrives   leaves   half past   o'clock   quarter past   quarter to

The Corner Store Closed until

1 The shop will re-open at _____

_____ .

Next trip to the ISLAND

2 The boat _____

_____ .

FLIGHT 618 DEPARTS

3 The aircraft _____

_____ .

Express from LIVERPOOL due at

4 The train _____

_____ .

MYSTERY TOUR starts

5 The coach _____

_____ .

MEET HERE ON SUNDAY AT

6 The cycling club _____

_____ .

SUNRISE   **SUNSET**

7 The sun _____

_____ .

POOL OPEN TODAY
from   to

8 The swimming-pool _____

_____ .

What are they made of?

Write the name of each object from the list in its correct panel.

a bell

a bolt

a comic

a cricket bat

a dagger

an envelope

a flagpole

a floorboard

the front of a
fish tank

goalposts

a horseshoe

a jam jar

a knife-blade

a lens

a magazine

a mallet

marbles

a milk bottle

a mirror

a nail

a newspaper

pages

a plank

a postage stamp

a poster

a five pound note

a screw

a sword

a tea-chest

a walking stick

a window pane

a windscreen

These are made of **glass**

These are made of **metal**

These are made of **paper**

These are made of **wood**

Five photographs

Five children have had their photographs taken.
They show them to each other. Here are the five.

Steven   **Kay**   **Larry**   **Holly**   **Thomas**

Each child explains what he, or she, was doing and where the photograph was taken.

A

outside the church
walking with my Dad
playing cricket
standing with my new bike
sitting on the diving board

B

outside my house
at the swimming pool
in my bridesmaid's dress
in the woods
on the sands

What they said has been mixed up in the two panels, **A** and **B**.
Put together the correct parts of **A** and **B** and write what each one said.

Steven   — "I am _____"

Kay   — "I am _____"

Larry   — "I am _____"

Holly   — "I am _____"

Thomas   — "I am _____"

C   If you have a favourite photograph of yourself write a sentence about it.
Explain what you were doing and where the photograph was taken.

_____

_____

Find a letter — make a word

By putting one letter in front of **arm**, you can make **farm** or **harm** or **warm**.
In the same way find the correct letter to write in front of each of these. The word you make must fit the clue.

ear

__ear — may be a grizzly

__ear — opposite of cheap

__ear — to be afraid

__ear — slang for clothing

__ear — listen

__ear — not far away

__ear — a fruit

__ear — at the back

__ear — a water-drop from the eyes

__ear — to put clothes on

__ear — twelve months

age

__age — a prison of bars

__age — in a book

__age — anger

__age — a herb

__age — payment for work

aid

__aid — put down

__aid — a girl

__aid — money had been given

__aid — a sudden attack

__aid — spoken

old

__old — brave

__old — opposite of hot

__old — to double something over

__old — a precious metal

__old — to grasp in your hand

__old — exchanged for money

__old — informed

eat

__eat — to strike

__eat — hotness

__eat — beef, or pork, or lamb

__eat — clean and tidy

__eat — cut out of the ground for fuel, or gardens

Words for pictures

candles	handle	label	parcel	table
cattle	kennel	medal	sandals	thistle

From this list write the correct name under each picture.

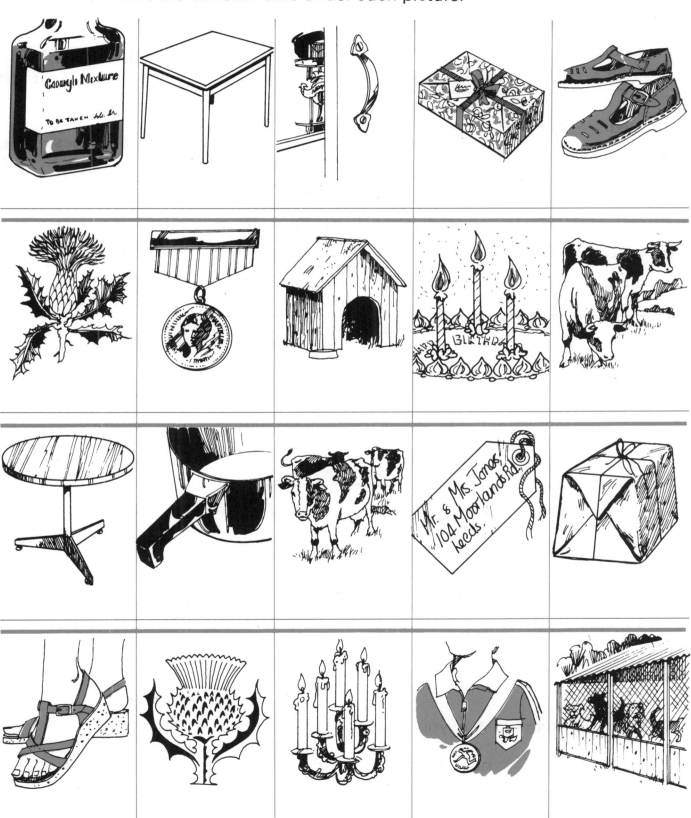

Placings

A The picture shows the finish of the Class 2 50-metre flat race.

In each of the sentences write the correct name of the child.

Wayne   Karen   Ann   Daren   Jan

1   In the race_____ was **first**,_____ was **second**,

_____ was **third**,_____ was **fourth** and_____ was **fift**

2   _____ was the **winner**,   6   _____ was the **slowest** runner

3   _____ was the **runner-up**.   7   _____ took the **longest** time.

4   _____ was **last**.   8   _____ took the **shortest** time.

5   _____ was the **fastest** runner.

B Here are some test results for the same five children.

Test Results

Name	Mathematics	Spelling	Total
Ann	8	17	
Daren	9	16	
Karen	7	19	
Jan	10	15	
Wayne	6	18	

From these results, write the correct names in each of these sentences.

1   In Mathematics,_____ did **best** and was **top**._____ did **worst** and was **bottom**.

2   In Spelling,_____ had the **highest** mark and_____ had the **lowest**.

3   _____ came **third** in both Mathematics and Spelling.

Add the marks for Mathematics and Spelling together for each child. Write the answers under Total. Write the correct names in the sentences.

4   _____ had the **highest** total marks and_____ had the **lowest**.

5   Equal **second** were _____

Alphabetical order — second letter

a	
b	
c	
z	

A Complete the alphabet, writing a small letter in each square.

B All these girls' names start with the letter E.

Ellie   **Et**hel   **Ei**leen   **En**id   **Ed**ie

To arrange them in alphabetical order, look at the second letter in each name.

The correct order is **Ed**ie, **Ei**leen, **El**lie, **En**id, **Et**hel.

Arrange the words in each of these groups in **alphabetical order**.

1

Clifford	1
Cecil	2
Cyril	3
Colin	4
Charles	5

2

Sinclair	1
Slade	2
Saunders	3
Schofield	4
Skinner	5

3

Didcot	1
Dudley	2
Dedham	3
Dartmouth	4
Doncaster	5

4

Woking	1
Wickford	2
Whalley	3
Wedmore	4
Walsall	5

5

robber	1
riddle	2
rugby	3
railway	4
record	5

6

teeth	1
thief	2
tourist	3
target	4
ticket	5

7

horse	1
hammer	2
hyena	3
herd	4
hurry	5

8

mustard	1
method	2
market	3
model	4
mistake	5

Actions

Choose the correct word from the group of three to write under each picture. The word tells what **action** is taking place.

carving
cooking
covering

1

2

3

catching
chasing
colliding

4

5

6

calling
curling
cutting

7

8

9

clowning
crooning
crowning

10

11

12

chiming
climbing
coming

13

14

15

Sentences about actions

These are the **endings** of sentences about the **actions** on page 14.

are colliding at the crossroads	is cutting his hedge
is crowning the May Queen	is coming down the road
is carving the meat	are climbing a tree
is calling to her family	is crooning into a microphone
are chiming in the belfry	is cooking a meal
is chasing a cat	is catching a ball
is curling her hair	is covering the birdcage
are clowning in the playground	

Write the correct ending for the sentence about each picture. The first one is done for you.

1 Mum___*is carving the meat*_____.

2 Dad_____.

3 Larry_____.

4 Rex, the dog, _____.

5 Two cars_____.

6 Josh_____.

7 The gardener_____.

8 Mum_____.

9 Laura_____.

10 The pop star_____.

11 The mayor_____.

12 Roy and his friends_____.

13 Two boys_____.

14 The bells_____.

15 The double-decker bus_____.

Words which sound the same

From each pair of words choose the correct one to write in each sentence.

1 **pail**   Jack went up the hill to fetch a_____ of water.

  pale   After he had fallen he looked very_____.

2 **bare**   Years ago you could sometimes see a dancing_____.

  bear   Men used to box with_____ fists.

3 **right**   As you_____ in this book, you fill up the lines

  write   from left to_____.

4 **peace**   The messenger held up a_____ of paper and said,

  piece   ''It will not be war but_____.''

5 **die**   Take care when washing a cheap dress or the_____ may run.

  dye   It was cruel to leave the wounded stag to_____.

6 **meat**   If you_____ me at the corner, we can go to the

  meet   butcher's shop together to buy our_____ for the week-end.

7 **pain**   John thought that the window was open. He felt a sharp

  pane   _____ when his hand went through the_____ of glass.

8 **sail**   We liked the boat which was for_____ but it

  sale   only had one_____.

9 **weak**   After a_____ without food the traveller felt

  week   very_____.

10 **wait**   We had to_____ at the post office until

  weight   the_____ of the parcel had been checked.

Words for pictures

From this list write the correct name under each picture.

actor	anchor	conjuror	doctor	tailor
alligator	conductor	corridor	razor	tractor

Placings

The family in this picture are watching a cricket match.

LEFT   **RIGHT**

Ann   David   Dad   Paul   Mum

Answer these questions by writing the name of the person.

1 Who is sitting in the middle?_____

2 Who is standing at the end of the row on the left?_____

3 Who is standing between Mum and Dad?_____

4 Who is sitting at the end of the row on the right?_____

5 Who is standing between Ann and Dad?_____

6 Who is on the right of David?_____

7 Who is on the right of Dad?_____

8 Who is on the left of Dad?_____

9 Who is on the left of Mum?_____

10 Who is on the right of Paul?_____

11 Who is on the left of David?_____

After a time, Ann goes and sits on the right of Mum.

12 Who is then at the end of the row on the left?_____

13 Who is then on the left of Ann?_____

14 Who then has only one person on his left?_____

15 Who is then in the middle of the row?_____

Biggest and smallest

animals   birds   shapes   ships   trees   vehicles

From the pictures and from this list write the correct word in each sentence.

circle   **triangle**   **square**

1   Here are three_____.
2   The_____ is the biggest and the_____ is the smallest.
3   The_____ is bigger than the_____ but is smaller than the_____.

mouse   **lion**   **elephant**

1   Here are three_____.
2   The_____ is the biggest and the_____ is the smallest.
3   The_____ is bigger than the_____ but is smaller than the_____.

launch   **tug**   **tanker**

1   Here are three_____.
2   The_____ is the biggest and the_____ is the smallest.
3   The_____ is bigger than the_____ but is smaller than the_____.

eagle   **wren**   **blackbird**

1   Here are three_____.
2   The_____ is the biggest and the_____ is the smallest.
3   The_____ is bigger than the_____ but is smaller than the_____.

ambulance   **car**   **coach**

1   Here are three_____.
2   The_____ is the biggest and the_____ is the smallest.
3   The_____ is bigger than the_____ but is smaller than the_____.

birch   **rose**   **oak**

1   Here are three_____.
2   The_____ is the biggest and the_____ is the smallest.
3   The_____ is bigger than the_____ but is smaller than the_____.

Words beginning with bl

From the clues given, find the words starting with **bl**.
Write one letter in each square.

1

as

				k

as soot

2

									y

— a hedgerow fruit

3

handle

				e

4

My nose is
beginning to

			d

5

The

				d

man
has a guide-dog.

6

After pulling on the rope,
I have a painful

							r

on my finger.

7

I had to fight my way
home through a snow

			z	z			

8

He is dark but she has

				d

hair.

9

Mum is wearing
her new striped

					e

10

The cheap pen
has made a

			t

on my book.

11

— Add bird to your first answer.

12

— He shoes horses and works at his anvil.

13

— This is on my handkerchief in picture 4.

14

— Do this to fill your balloon with air.

15

— If your penknife is like this, it needs sharpening.